CHAPTER 17

is a planet where magic reigns supreme. For centuries the world has been ruled by the seven major Guilds, or schools, of magic, each presided over by a Guild Master. Each respective Master serves as the living receptacle for an eternal spirit embodying that particular Guild's sorcerous knowledge.

Despite her family's ties to the Nouveau Guild, socialite Giselle Villard's disinterest in magic bordered on disdain. However, Giselle's older sister Genevieve dutifully applied herself to magical studies and stood poised to become Master of the Nouveau Guild. But at Gen's Rite of Ascension, Giselle's palm was imprinted with a mysterious sigil that somehow trapped the eternal spirits of all seven Guilds within her. Granted vast magical might, Giselle defeated the Masters in a battle for control of the spirits and became the most powerful Mystic her world has ever known.

RECENTLY

Giselle brought Thierry Chevalier, the artist who had tried to befriend her just after she was granted the sigil, to her sanctum on the moon and revealed everything that had befallen her. Just as it appeared Thierry and Giselle would embrace, Gen arrived.

Within moments the group was attacked by a magic-absorbing creature, set free, supposedly by accident, by Giselle's pet squit, Skitter. Giselle ultimately destroyed the creature by utilizing her sigil in an untried manner — rather than generating magical spells, she found she could channel raw energy through the sigil. Pleased with her newfound knowledge, Giselle rejoined Thierry while Gen pondered Skitter's true purpose.

Ron MARZ
WRITER

Fabrizio FIORENTINO
PENCILER

Matt RYAN
INKER

Elizabeth LEWIS
COLORIST

Dave LANPHEAR
LETTERER

TABLE OF CONTENTS

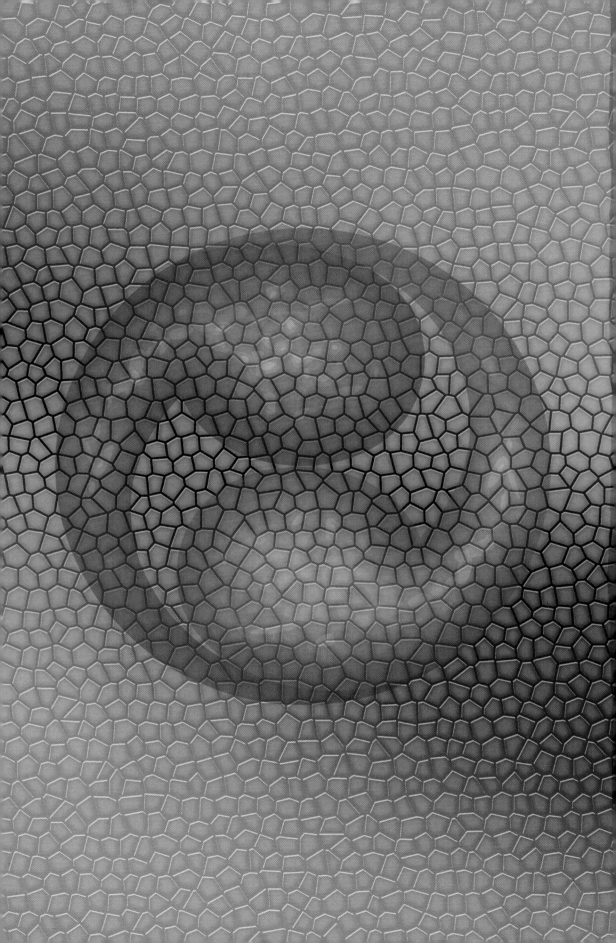

SO WHAT DO WE HAVE TODAY, JULIAN?

[.|.|']

THE MASTERS OF THREE ANCILLARY GUILDS ARE MAKING OFFICIAL VISITS.

THEY ARRIVED A SHORT TIME AGO AND I'VE ALREADY GREETED THEM.

THEY AWAIT YOU IN THE LeCAVALIER SANCTUARY.

YOU RECEIVED THE SCROLLS BRIEFING YOU AS TO THE INDIVIDUAL GUILDS AND MASTERS?

I DID.

OSTENSIBLY, OF COURSE, THEY'RE HERE TO PAY THEIR RESPECTS TO NOUVEAU'S NEW MASTER.

BUT THEY'RE CERTAINLY HOPING TO TAKE ADVANTAGE OF YOUR INEXPERIENCE AND IMPROVE THEIR RESPECTIVE ALLIANCES.

[.|.|']

KEEP AN EYE ON THAT ONE. HE CONCERNS ME.

YES, SIR.

NOUVEAU HAS A LONG TRADITION OF EQUITABLE RELATIONSHIPS WITH THE ANCILLARIES.

I HAVE NO INTENTION OF CHANGING THAT POLICY.

WE THREE...

...SAMEDI, DRAGON, PROTEAN...

...COULD FORM A POWERFUL BLOCK IF ALIGNED WITH *ANY ONE* OF THE MAJOR GUILDS.

FIRST WE LISTEN TO WHAT NOUVEAU HAS TO OFFER.

THOUGH I *WOULD* BE MORE COMFORTABLE HAVING SUCH DISCUSSIONS IN A PRIVATE SETTING.

OF COURSE. WE CAN CONTINUE OUR CONVERSATION IN THE GARDENS. THEY'VE ALWAYS BEEN MY FAVORITE ASPECT OF THE CATHEDRAL.

JULIAN, IF YOU AND THE GUARDS WOULD LEAVE US FOR A TIME?

I'M NOT SURE BEING ALONE WITH THEM IS THE WISEST CHOICE, MASTER VILLARD.

AT LEAST PERMIT *ME* TO ACCOMPANY—

THEY'RE OUR *GUESTS*, JULIAN. IT'S FINE.

I HOPE THAT'S TRUE.

NOW...

...YOU HAVE ME ALL TO YOURSELVES.

PLEASE, SPEAK CANDIDLY.

BEAR IN MIND, MASTER VILLARD, WE SPEAK NOT SOLELY FOR OURSELVES, BUT FOR *ALL* THE ANCILLARY GUILDS.

YOUR ASCENSION IS BEING VIEWED AS AN OPPORTUNITY TO CORRECT THE INJUSTICES OF THE PAST.

IT'S HOPED *YOU* WILL HAVE THE COURAGE TO BE AN AGENT OF CHANGE.

THE ATTACKER CHOSE TO *PERISH* RATHER THAN BE TAKEN.

TO KEEP US FROM LEARNING THE TRUTH BEHIND THE ASSASSINATION PLOT.

WHAT OF THE OTHER MASTERS?

WE ARE NOT TO BLAME!

I ASSURE YOU, WE KNEW *NOTHING* OF THIS.

RELEASE THEM.

IT'S OBVIOUS WE'VE *ALL* BEEN THE VICTIMS OF DUPLICITY.

YES, BUT *WHOSE?*

THAT'S WHAT CONCERNS ME MOST, JULIAN. WE HAVE AN ENEMY OUT THERE...

...AND NO IDEA WHO IT IS.

RUSE

ARCADIAN

ARCHARD BAFFLED!
CRIME SPREE HITS CITY:

FAMED
DETECTIVE
FAILS!

LATEST
CRIMES
A PUZZLE!

MURDERS FOUND

CHAPTER 2

The PENNY ARCADIAN

Copiously Illustrated   Afternoon Edition, Price One Penny

DOCKYARD DISASTER

MYSTERY SHIP SET ABLAZE

❧ OUR PLAYERS ❧

SIMON ARCHARD

THE CITY'S FAVORITE SON, HIS MIND IS RAZOR-SHARP

EMMA BISHOP

A FETCHING BEAUTY, HER SPIRIT CRAVES ADVENTURE

MIRANDA CROSS

A MYSTERIOUS VISITOR, SHE EXHIBITS A CERTAIN MAGIC

WEIRD VESSEL RENT ASUNDER!

A sailing ship secretly ferrying an indeterminate quantity of illegal opiates caught fire following a mysterious explosion from deep within its holds.

Inside the ship at the time of the explosion were sleuth and scrutator Simon Archard and his assistant Emma Bishop. Archard had summoned the local constabularies dockside to gather evidence of the opiates, which seamen of unknown origin were caught smuggling to Partington's shores inside the bellies of market-bound fish. While grateful for Archard's help in quelling the smuggling operation, authorities admit it has doubtless been in process for some weeks previous.

Though no police fatalities were reported following the blast, the whereabouts of Archard and Bishop are at this presstime unknown. •••PLEASE CONTINUE INSIDE

Mark **WAID** WRITER   Butch **GUICE** PENCILER   Michael **PERKINS** & the Agents of Archard INKERS   Laura **DePUY** COLORIST   Dave **LANPHEAR** LETTERER

DESPITE SIMON'S IMPATIENT TOE-TAPPING, I REPAIR TO MY QUARTERS FOR A QUICK *BATH* AND CHANGE OF *CLOTHING.*

I SUPPOSE I COULD BE MOVING MORE *QUICKLY,* BUT I KNOW WHAT COMES *NEXT.*

VOTES FOR WOMEN

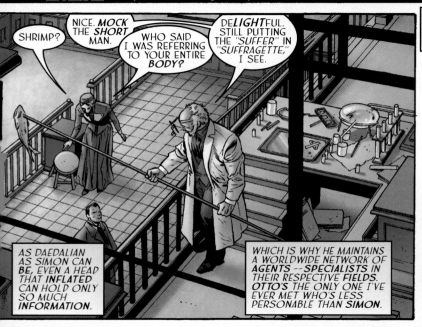

SHRIMP?

NICE. *MOCK* THE *SHORT* MAN.

WHO SAID I WAS REFERRING TO YOUR ENTIRE *BODY?*

DE*LIGHT*FUL. STILL PUTTING THE "*SUFFER*" IN "*SUFFRAGETTE*," I SEE.

AS DAEDALIAN AS SIMON CAN *BE,* EVEN A HEAD THAT *INFLATED* CAN HOLD ONLY SO MUCH *INFORMATION.*

WHICH IS WHY HE MAINTAINS A WORLDWIDE NETWORK OF *AGENTS* -- *SPECIALISTS* IN THEIR RESPECTIVE *FIELDS.* *OTTO'S* THE ONLY ONE I'VE EVER MET WHO'S LESS *PERSONABLE* THAN *SIMON.*

I CAN'T *BELIEVE* WE USED TO *DATE.*

SO I'M SEARCHING FOR ELEMENTS *FOREIGN* TO OUR SHORES.

SOMETHING I CAN TRACE TO A SPECIFIC *REGION* WOULD BE MOST HELPFUL.

CERTAINLY. THERE MUST BE A *TOY SHOPPE* SOMEWHERE IN THE NEIGHBORHOOD.

AND I AM NOT SIMON'S *SCRIVENER!* I AM HIS *PARTNER!*

ASSISTANT.

READ THE *NEWSPAPERS.*

EXAMINE THE *BUSINESS CARDS.*

QUITE THE *CHANGE* FROM YOUR *OLD* PARTNER, SIMON. WHAT WAS HIS *NAME* AGAIN? *LIGHT*SOMETHING...

TWELVE GALLONS OF *ACID* IN A FOUR-GALLON *JAR*.

I *HATE* FISH.

OTTO PRESSMONK, ESQ.

CHEMIST

I HATE *CLAMS* AND I HATE *OYSTERS* AND I HATE *COD* AND I HATE--

NOT ASKING FOR MUCH, ARE WE?

FIRST, TO SEPARATE THE DRUG'S *COMPONENTS*. JUST A DRAM OF *THERONIUM IODINE...*

I THINK YOU MEAN *"IODIDE."*

MY *MISTAKE.*

HMMM. AN *UNUSUAL* CHAIN OF *FERROUS MOLECULES...*

SIMON, I'LL *BE A WHILE.*

TELL YOUR *SECRETARY* TO COME BY LATER FOR MY *FINDINGS.*

AND ORDER HER TO *REPLACE* MY *CHAIR.*

LIGHTBOURNE.

THE WAY SIMON *SPEAKS* IT SPREADS *GOOSEFLESH* ACROSS MY SKIN.

I'VE HEARD RUMORS... *EVERYONE'S* HEARD *RUMORS...* BUT I'VE NEVER ASKED SIMON *DIRECTLY* ABOUT MY *PREDECESSOR...* OR THE WAY HE *DIED.*

BACK *TO* IT, OTTO. EMMA WILL VISIT YOU AROUND *NOON.*

AND *NO,* I DON'T WISH TO *TALK* ABOUT IT.

ABOUT *WHAT?*

YOU WERE PREPARING TO INQUIRE ABOUT *LIGHTBOURNE.*

YOU *ARE* GOOD.

ON THE WALK BACK TO HEADQUARTERS, SIMON GROWS INCREASINGLY *REMOTE* AND *WITHDRAWN.*

I DON'T TAKE IT *PERSONALLY,* EVEN AFTER I'M FORCED TO GUIDE HIM BY THE *ELBOW.*

I DO, HOWEVER, WALK HIM THROUGH THE OCCASIONAL *PUDDLE* JUST FOR THE FUN OF IT.

UNDER THOSE RARE CIRCUMSTANCES WHERE SIMON IS *TRULY* PERPLEXED, HE HONES HIS CONCENTRATION BY CLAMBERING INSIDE A BEASTLY CONTRAPTION OF HIS OWN DESIGN--

--A SORT OF *REVERSE BATHYSPHERE* DESIGNED TO DEPRIVE HIM OF EXTRANEOUS *SENSORY INPUT.*

HE CALLS IT HIS *"THINK TANK."* WHILE I CANCEL HIS *APPOINTMENTS* FOR THE DAY...

...HE PREPARES FOR *IMMERSION.*

HMMM.

CAN'T YOU SLIP INTO A *HOT BATH* LIKE EVERYONE *ELSE?*

SIMON?

WHAT? OH. I WASN'T *LISTENING.*

SHOCKING. YOU KNOW HOW I FEEL ABOUT THAT... THAT *RECEPTACLE.*

YOU'RE *WORRIED* FOR ME.

A BIT.

DO YOU REMEMBER WHAT WE CALL THAT?

"AN EGREGIOUS OUTPOURING OF IRKSOME EMOTION?"

PRECISELY.

WHEN SHALL I SAY YOU'LL BE *AVAILABLE* AGAIN?

WHEN I *AM.*

MEANWHILE, YOU'LL LUNCH WITH THE *COMMISSIONER?*

WITH *PLEASURE.* UNLIKE *SOME* IN YOUR ACQUAINTANCE...

"...HE'S *ALWAYS* GLAD TO SEE ME."

WHAT DO YOU WANT *NOW*?

OH, *MY*. THEOPOLOUS, I APOLOGIZE IF I'VE COME AT AN *INOPPORTUNE* TIME...

NO. NO, IN FACT, I HAVE A MESSAGE OF SOME *IMPORT* FOR YOU *AND* YOUR PARTNER.

AS YOU KNOW, THIS DEPARTMENT HAS TRADITIONALLY EXTENDED TO YOU TWO *EVERY COURTESY*. I, *PERSONALLY*, HAVE CONSIDERED YOU MY *FRIENDS*.

LIKEWISE, THEOP--

NO *MORE*.

... WHAT?

ON HIS *OWN, WITHOUT* AUTHORIZATION, SIMON SIMPLY *COMMANDEERED* A BAND OF *MY OFFICERS* LAST NIGHT!

BUT WITH GOOD *REASON*--

I DON'T *CARE!* IT'S NOT THE *FIRST* TIME HE'S TAKEN *TOTAL LIBERTY* WITH *MY* DEPARTMENT-- BUT IT *IS* THE *LAST*!

DO YOU *HEAR* ME?

EFFECTIVE *IMMEDIATELY*, THERE WILL BE *NO SPECIAL FAVORS* GRANTED BY THIS OFFICE... AND *NO CONSIDERATIONS*.

THEOPOLOUS, THIS DOESN'T *SOUND* LIKE YOU.

THEN PERHAPS YOU NEED A NEW *AUDIOLOGIST*.

I AM THE LAW IN PARTINGTON...

...*NOT* SIMON ARCHARD!

*S*OMETHING'S NOT RIGHT.

AND SO THE AFTERNOON. WHEREVER I GO, A GRUFF RECEPTION.

IT'S AS IF ALL THE MEN OF POWER IN PARTINGTON ABANDONED THEIR REGARD FOR SIMON AND HIS DOINGS OVERNIGHT.

OR, RATHER, I SHOULD SAY OVER NIGHTS...TWO...COINCIDING WITH THE ARRIVAL OF BARONESS MIRANDA CROSS TO OUR CITY...

...AND NO DETECTIVE WORTH A FIG TAKES COINCIDENCE SERIOUSLY.

...AND HOW WAS SHE ABLE TO RESIST MY CONTROL?

...IS... MY GOD...

A DISCREET **CARRIAGE RIDE** BRINGS ME TO HER ESTATE-IN-**PROCESS** --AN ABANDONED CASTLE WHICH CREWS HAVE BEGUN **REFURBISHING** TO HER QUESTIONABLE TASTE.

WHAT DID I **EXPECT** BY **COMING** HERE? THAT SHE WOULD INVITE ME IN FOR **TEA** SO THAT SHE MIGHT **EXPLAIN** HERSELF...

SHE SEEMS TO HAVE POWERS TO MATCH MY **OWN**...TO **EXCEED** THEM...BUT **THAT** IS INFORMATION I HAVE NO CHOICE BUT TO KEEP **PRIVATE**.

I CANNOT CONFER WITH SIMON ABOUT WHAT I SAW DURING THE **FIRE** WITHOUT REVEALING MY **OWN** SECRETS -- AND I **CANNOT** YET TELL SIMON ABOUT MY ABILITIES. I **CAN NOT**. THE **CONSEQUENCES**...

BEFORE LAST NIGHT, THE PRICE FOR THEIR USE WAS **FORFEITURE** OF ALL I **KNOW**. NOW, APPARENTLY, THE COST IS THAT THE BARONESS WILL TAKE THEM FOR HER **OWN**...OR SO SHE **SAYS**...AND, PRESUMABLY, USE THEM **AGAINST** US.

SHE MAY BE **LYING**. BUT FOR **SIMON'S** SAKE, I CANNOT TAKE THAT **RISK**.

WHY WOULD SHE WISH US **HARM**? DID HER PRESENCE ON THE **FISHING BOAT** PROVE A CONNECTION TO ILLICIT **ACTIVITIES**?

AND HOW IS SHE BEHIND THE SUDDEN **SEA CHANGE** IN SIMON'S **POPULARITY**? HOW COULD **ANY** MAN BE INFLUENCED BY A WOMAN WITH SUCH OBVIOUSLY GAUDY AND ECCENTRIC **TASTES**?

WHY, THAT GHASTLY WINDOW **ALONE** IS...

...IS EVIDENCE.

I HAVE TO **GO**. I HAVE TO REPORT THIS TO SIMON...

...BEFORE I AM **SEEN**.

"I **TOLD** YOU, ANTAEUS..."

...I CAN HEAR THAT SOW PRACTICALLY *MOOING* WITH FRUSTRATION.

I ALMOST EXPERIENCE A... *PITYING?* IS THAT THE WORD?... *PITYING.*

AFTER ALL, HER ONLY FUTURE *NOW* LIES IN BECOMING MY FAVORITE *PLAYTHING.*

I'M SORRY, *ANTAEUS.* MY *SECOND* FAVORITE.

OR *THIRD,* PUTTING *SIMON* IN THE COUNT...

♪ NOW, WHO HERE HAS SOMETHING *FOR ME..?* ♪

USSZZZZ?

YOU ARE MY EYES AND *EARS* IN THIS DREADFUL CITY. GO DO... *THAT.*

NEE*DULLL?*

OH, NO. THERE IS NO *NECESSITY* AT THE *MOMENT* FOR... DIRECT?... *DIRECT* ACTION, YES?

THERE MUST BE *PATIENCE.* THIS, YOU *UNDERSTAND?*

MY! I *HAVE* HIRED WELL, HAVE I NOT? AN *EMPTY* SYRINGE MEANS YOU'VE ELIMINATED ONE... *SMALL* COMPLICATION FOR US. EXCELLENT.

ALL GOES, ALL GOES. ANTAEUS, FINISH DELIVERING THE LITTLE *BOXES* TO THE *BIG* MEN.

AND TRY NOT TO *BREAK* ANY THIS TIME? IN FACT, *SAVE* YOUR STRENGTH.

GOOD BOYS.

AS PROMISED, MY RETURN TRIP TAKES ME PAST OTTO'S **LAB** TO RETRIEVE HIS **REPORT.**

Oh...!

THERE WON'T BE ONE.

THE BARONESS. I DON'T KNOW WHY, OR HOW...

...BUT SHE'S **BEHIND THIS.** I **KNOW** IT.

SERGEANT, WHO *DID* THIS?

LOOKS T'*ME* 'SIF 'E DID IT 'ISSELF, MIZ BISHOP.

WE GOT AN ANON'MOUS TIP WHAT *BROUGHT* US HERE AN' FOUND HIM *THUSLY.*

PROLLY REACHED TOO *HIGH,* HE DID... SIMPLY LOST 'IS *BALANCE* AN' THE CAB'NET TUMBLED *ATOP* 'IM. A RIGHT UNFORTUNATE *ACCIDENT.*

"ACCIDENT," MY LACE *SHEVIS.*

MYSTER[Y] EXPLOSIO[N] SINKS VES[SEL]

BUT BY THE TIME I MAKE MY WAY BACK TO *47 STRAND* TO TELL SIMON OF MY *FINDINGS...*

SIMON?

SIMON?

...HE'S NOWHERE TO BE *FOUND.*

STILL, OTTO WILL NOT GO *UNAVENGED.* SINCE SIMON LEFT NO NOTE TO THE *CONTRARY,* HE'LL NO DOUBT RETURN *PROMPTLY.*

THEN *AGAIN...*

A DAY LATER, I DON'T KNOW WHETHER TO BE WORRIED FOR OR ANGRY AT SIMON.

WHILE HARDLY A PARAGON OF **WARMTH**, HE'D STILL WANT TO BE **PRESENT** AS WE BURY ONE OF HIS **ASSOCIATES.** THIS, I **KNOW.**

TOO WELL.

HAS THE BARONESS ALSO GOTTEN TO SIMON SOMEHOW, WITHOUT DISCLOSING HER TRIUMPH TO ME?

I DOUBT IT. JUDGING BY HER BEHAVIOR AT THE **FIRE,** SHE'D WANT ME TO **KNOW.**

NO **AUTOPSY** WAS NECESSARY. THE AUTHORITIES, FRANKLY, COULDN'T **WAIT** TO GET OTTO INTO THE **GROUND.** BLESS HIS SOUL, HE COUNTED AMONG HIS COMPATRIOTS ONLY A HANDFUL OF SIMON'S FELLOW **OPERATIVES.** BARTLESBY THE MOUCH... THE ABBESS **LADYBIRD NELL**... A FEW OTHERS...

...HARDLY A FITTING **FUNEREAL PARTY** FOR EVEN A MAN OF OTTO'S SOUR DISPOSITION. IF HE HAD ANY **FAMILY...**

-- GATHERED HERE TO PAY **FINAL RESPECTS** TO THE DECEASED --

HAD T'GO HEARIN' ABOUT THIS IN THE **PENNYSHEETS,** Y'BLOODY **SHORTWANK...**

...LEF' ME QUITES AN **ITCH** T'SCRATCH WI' YE, BROTHER OTTO...!

THE **DEAD?** THERE AIN'T NO WORDS **FOUL** ENOUGH. YE THINK YERSELVES HIS **FRIENDS?** NO.

THAT'S WHAT I KEEP *TELLING* MYSELF.

...I'D BE *AMAZED*.

--A SOUL *RELEASED* FROM THIS MORTAL COIL TO BATHE IN THE LIGHT OF --

...LEAVIN' OUR *MUM* WI'OUT TWO COINS T'RUB *TOGETHER* F'R EVEN TH' *WARMTH* OF IT...

...YER *NIECES* 'N' *NEPHEWS* ALLUS IGNORED THO' I *BEGS* YE T'PUT *FOOD* IN THEIR HUNGRY MOUTHS...

MADAM, OUR *CONDOLENCES*. WE HAD *NO IDEA* OTTO HAD A *SISTER*...

..BUT *REGARDLESS* OF WHATEVER QUARRELS YOU *KNEW*, THE TWO OF YOU, WE *IMPLORE* YOU TO SPEAK NO ILL OF THE... THE...

THESE ARE ALL WHAT'S FIT T'SHARE THEIR TIME WI' *OTTO PRESSMONK!*

LET THE *MAGGOTS* BE WITH THEIR *OWN!*

OH, GOOD *LORD!* GET THEM *OFF!* *GET THEM OFF!*

WHILE THE ABBESS AND THE PRIEST RELIEVE THEMSELVES OF THE CONTENTS OF THEIR *STOMACHS*, WE TRY OUR *BEST* TO SALVAGE OTTO'S *DIGNITY*...

...BUT THERE ARE TOO *MANY* OF THE WRIGGLING *LARVAE*... AND THEY'LL FIND OTTO SOONER THAN LATER, *ANYWAY*. WITH GRIEF MORE PROFOUND THAN *BEFORE*, WE EASE OTTO INTO THE *EARTH*... AND SING A *PRAYER* THOUGH WE'RE ONE VOICE *SHORT*.

SIMON...

...WHERE *ARE* YOU?

CONTINUED NEXT ISSUE

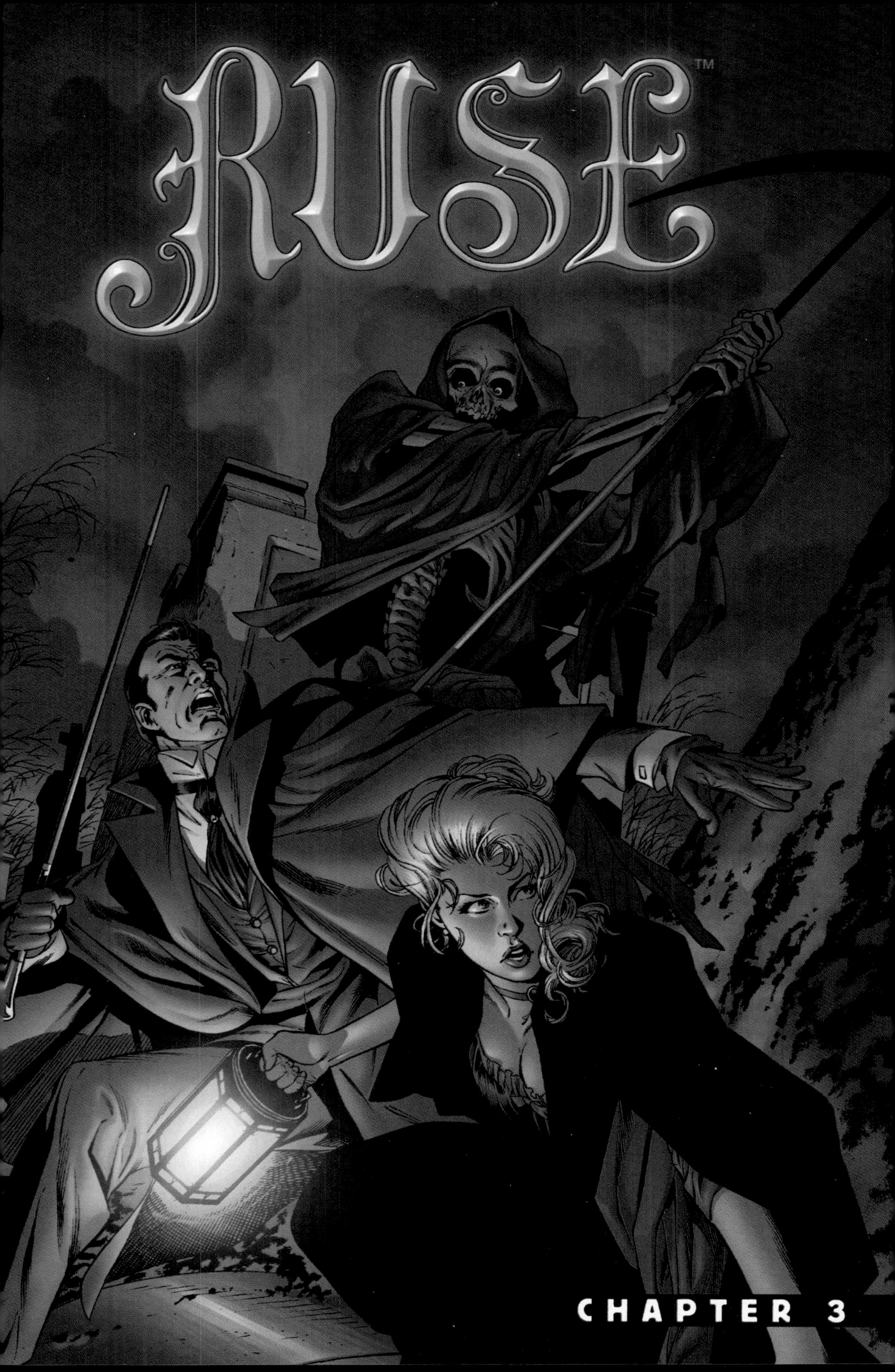
RUSE™
CHAPTER 3

I COULD HAVE TAKEN A CARRIAGE BACK FROM OTTO'S FUNERAL.

I ELECT TO WALK.

IT'LL DULL THE IMPULSE TO BURY SIMON RIGHT **NEXT** TO HIM.

EVEN THOUGH SIMON ARCHARD HURTLES THROUGH LIFE WITH THE COMPASSION OF A **THROWN BRICK**, IT'S **UNFORGIVABLE** THAT HE WOULD **IGNORE** A MEMORIAL SERVICE FOR ONE OF HIS **OWN OPERATIVES**.

IT'S NOT AS IF SIMON'S MET WITH FOUL PLAY **HIMSELF**. IF **THAT** WERE THE CASE, I WOULD HAVE... BEEN **NOTIFIED**.

BUT EVEN IF HE'S DOGMATICALLY FOLLOWING A NEW LEAD ON THE **OPIATE SMUGGLING** CASE, NOTHING -- AND I MEAN **NOTHING** -- KEEPS SIMON FROM **DEVOURING** THE WARES OF THE **CORNER NEWS VENDORS**.

SIMON **PRIDES** HIMSELF ON STAYING INFORMED ON ALL MATTERS REGARDING THE CITY OF PARTINGTON -- AND OTTO'S **DEATH** HEADLINED **EVERY BROADSHEET**.

WHICH BRINGS US BACK TO "UNFORGIVABLE."

HOWEVER, ONCE I LAY EYES ON **47 STRAND** ONCE MORE...

...SUDDENLY, BEATING AN **EXCUSE** OUT OF SIMON IS THE **LAST** THING ON MY MIND.

AS IT HAPPENS, WHILE I'VE BEEN BUSY CONDEMNING **SIMON**...

...SOMEONE **ELSE** HAS BEEN CONDEMNING HIS **HEADQUARTERS.**

WHAT THE **DEVIL**...?

OFFICER, WHAT'S THE **MEANING** OF THIS?

MISS **BISHOP,** IS IT? MISS BISHOP, WE'LL HAVE **NAE** TROUBLE HERE FROM THE LIKES O' **YOU.**

"THE **LIKES** OF..."?

WAIT. OVER **THERE.** THE MEN GIVING THE ORDERS--

-- THEY'RE THE **MAYOR** OF PARTINGTON -- **AND** THE **BANKER,** WHO --

--DECONSECRATED OR **NOT, NEVER** SHOULD HAVE SOLD SUCH A **SACRED** BUILDING TO SUCH A **PROFANE MARPLOT!** MY MOST SINCERE APOLOGIES, MAYOR!

I **AGREE** IT'S A **SIN** TO SEE THIS CATHEDRAL GO FROM **NO** USE TO **ILL** USE, PERTHANBY --

-- AND I'M INCLINED SIMPLY TO BURN IT TO THE **GROUND** TO ALLEVIATE THE STINK OF **HERESY** FROM ITS RAFTERS! YOU **HEARD** ME, MISS BISHOP!

BOTH OF THESE MEN HAVE ALWAYS BEEN STAUNCH **SUPPORTERS** OF SIMON'S ACTIVITIES. THEIR SUDDEN **TURNABOUT** PERPLEXES ME...

...UNTIL I SEE THEM DIP **SNUFF** FROM BOXES OF A CHILLINGLY **FAMILIAR** DESIGN...

...ONE THAT MARKS THEM AS *GIFTS* FROM THE BARONESS *MIRANDA CROSS*... *IMPORTER* OF THE OPIATE HIDDEN *IN THE SNUFF*...A DRUG WHICH APPARENTLY ALLOWS HER SOME MEASURE OF *CONTROL* OVER THOSE WHO *PARTAKE* OF IT.

AND WHERE, DEAR GIRL, *IS* YOUR EMPLOYER? I WAS LOOKING *FORWARD* TO *PERSONALLY* RUNNING HIM OUT OF *TOWN*...

...WITH *YOU* NOT FAR *BEHIND!*

I *ASSURE* YOU, MAYOR, I'VE NO MORE IDEA WHERE MY *PARTNER* IS THAN DO *YOU*...

...BUT AS THIS IS THE MOST LOGICAL SITE FOR HIS *RETURN*, I'VE *EVERY RIGHT* AS A *LAW-ABIDING CITIZEN* TO WAIT FOR HIM *HERE.*

IF YOU WISH ME TO *LEAVE*, YOU'LL HAVE TO *PHYSICALLY REMOVE* ME FROM --

--*OH!*

THIS WAY, MISSY. AND STOP *SQUIRMING.* I HAVE A TOUCH OF THE *SCIATICA.*

SCIATICA?

IT'S A PINCHED NERVE CON--

I KNOW WHAT SCIATICA IS, YOU OX! PUT ME DOWN!

WITH PLEASURE.

SHE'S ALL *YOURS*, BOSS.

ENJOY.

"WHERE HAVE YOU *BEEN?*"

"CERTAINLY, *SOMEONE'S* BEHIND OUR CURRENT DIFFICULTIES."

"WHERE HAVE YOU *BEEN?*"

"THE BARONESS IS AS VIABLE A *SUSPECT* AS *ANY.*"

"WHERE HAVE YOU *BEEN?*"

"PARTICULARLY SINCE SHE AND THE *OPIATE* HIT OUR SHORES *SIMULTANEOUSLY.*"

"*WHERE HAVE YOU BEEN?*"

...

OUT.

WHAT HAVE YOU *LEARNED?*

THAT YOU'RE A *HORSE'S ARSE.* ALSO NOT *NEWS.*

SIMON, MIRANDA CROSS HAS BEEN HANDING OUT *GIFT TINS* OF DRUG-LACED *SNUFF.* THE POLICE COMMISSIONER AND LORD *WAINSCOTT* ARE NOW IN HER *THRALL.*

WORSE, SHE'S MADE THE *BANKER* AND THE *MAYOR* HER PUPPETS, AS *WELL*--

--BECAUSE MEN SUCH AS *THOSE* ARE THE PILLARS OF *SOCIETY.* IF PARTINGTON'S *POWER BROKERS* ARE DOING HER *BIDDING,* WE MAY AS WELL CHANGE THE CITY'S NAME TO *CROSSTON.*

NO!

SIMON, *NO!* THAT WAS *YOU?* IN DISGUISE?

THAT OTTO WAS *MURDERED,* I HAVE NO *DOUBT.*

BUT SINCE WE'RE BEING LED TO BELIEVE *OTHERWISE,* I CHOSE TO KEEP MY INVESTIGATION *LOW-PROFILE.*

I WOULDN'T *COUNT* ON IT, BARONESS! YES, I *KNOW* IT'S *YOU!*

AND I *SWEAR* TO YOU BY ALL THAT IS *HOLY* THAT YOU WILL DERIVE *NO PLEASURE* FROM MY *PRESENCE!*

THIS IS *NEWS?*

I'M *OVERPAYING* YOU.

TAP TAP

SIMON!

OF COURSE. NOW...

...WHAT'S THIS ABOUT THE *BARONESS MIRANDA...?*

I WISH THIS CAME AS LESS OF A *REVELATION* TO YOU. I *ASSUMED* YOU WERE *INVESTIGATING* THIS *VERY NOTION. THAT* WOULD BE YOUR *ONLY EXCUSE* FOR MISSING OTTO'S *FUNERAL.*

IT WAS *BLEAK* AND *HORRIBLE,* SIMON. SOME OLD *CRONE* EVEN THREW A FISTFUL OF--OF--

MAGGOTS?

YES! MAGGOTS INTO THE *COFFIN* AND --

-- WAIT. HOW DID YOU KNOW *THAT?*

BECAUSE THEY TOOK ALL *NIGHT* TO GATHER.

SO WHAT HAVE *YOU* LEARNED?

NOTHING.

YET.

THAT'S WHAT THE *MAGGOTS* ARE FOR.

AND...? THAT CRIES *OUT* FOR EXPLANATION!

YOU WON'T LIKE IT.

LET ME BE THE JUDGE OF --

⇒SNIFF⇐ ⇒SNIFF⇐

SIMON, IS THAT *CAMPHOR?*

YES. I'VE SPREAD SOME UNDER MY NOSE. I SUGGEST YOU DO THE SAME.

WHY?

⇒HHUH⇐
⇒HHHHUH⇐ EXPLAIN TO ME *AGAIN*

⇒HHHUH⇐

WHY *I'M* NOT PLAYING LOOKOUT AND THE

⇒HHHUH⇐

CARRIAGE DRIVER ISN'T DOING THE *DIGGING?*

YOU *WANTED* TO BE A DETECTIVE.

CHONK

HELLO, OTTO.

I'VE BEEN THINKING, THOUGH. IF OTTO WAS, IN FACT, MURDERED, IT WAS BECAUSE WE WENT TO HIM IN SEARCH OF *ANSWERS.*

WHICH MEANS *WE* WERE BEING *WATCHED.*

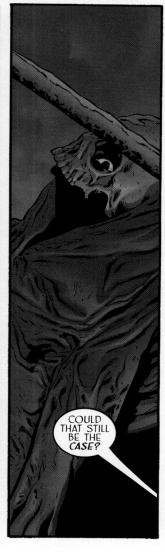

COULD THAT STILL BE THE *CASE?*

NOT ALL OF SIMON'S OPERATIVES ARE ON A *PAYROLL*. MANY OF THE LESS FREQUENTLY *CONSULTED*-- PARTICULARLY THOSE WHO ARE WELL-TO-DO *THEMSELVES*--LEND THEIR SERVICES IN EXCHANGE FOR PAST *FAVORS*.

HEADMASTER *WARREN SUMMERSBY* OF *PARTINGTON UNIVERSITY*, FOR EXAMPLE.

AT SIMON'S BEHEST, SUMMERSBY KEEPS WATCH OVER HIS BEST AND BRIGHTEST STUDENTS WITH AN EYE TOWARDS WHICH ONES MAY, IN TIME, BECOME EITHER *ALLIES* OR *ADVERSARIES*.

ASTOUNDING.

OTTO *CONTINUES* TO AID US FROM BEYOND THE *GRAVE*. HE--

THE DAMAGE TO OTTO'S *BODY* WAS *INCONSISTENT* WITH THE SIZE OF THE SHELF THAT "FELL" ON HIM. SINCE THERE WAS NO *AUTOPSY* AND OTTO WAS, FOLLOWING HIS PROCLAIMED WISHES, BURIED *SANS ENBALMING*...

...THE MAGGOTS WERE MY WAY OF LEECHING ENOUGH FLUID FROM OTTO'S *SYSTEM* TO DETERMINE IF HE WAS *POISONED* RATHER THAN *CRUSHED*.

AND HE *WAS*.

MOREOVER, THE LARVAE AND THIS *SMUGGLED PHIAL* TEST CONSISTENTLY WITH EACH *OTHER*. THIS INDICATES THAT OTTO WAS INJECTED WITH A FATAL DOSE OF THE VERY OPIATE THE BARONESS IS USING TO MANIPULATE HER *VICTIMS*.

AVAILED NEITHER OF *OTTO'S* LABORATORY NOR HIS *OWN*, SIMON ASKS FOR AND IS GRANTED TEMPORARY ACCESS TO THE *SCHOOL'S* FACILITIES, BUT...

...WE HAVEN'T MUCH *TIME*. THE *STUDENTS* WILL ARRIVE SHORTLY, AND I'D RATHER NOT HAVE TO DEAL WITH THEIR *FAWNING ADMIRATION*. IT'S QUITE THE *NUISANCE*.

WHAT?

NOTHING.

AAAAH! SIMON, THEY'RE *FLYING*--!

TKK TKK TKK TKK TKK TKK TKK TKK TKK TKK

NO. NO, THEY'RE *CLINGING* TO THE *METAL RIM* OF THE *MAGNIFYING LENS*.

THE DRUG... MADE THEM... *MAGNETIC?* THAT'S --

FASCINATING.

I WAS GOING TO SAY "*REVOLTING*"... BUT HOW DOES THAT FIT IN WITH THIS NOTION OF *MENTAL CONTROL?*

WE'LL ASK *ADELINE*.

HOW MANY *OPERATIVES* DO YOU *HAVE*...?

...AND DISTRACT HER *MOTHER* WHILE I ARRANGE A *CONFERENCE.*

DISTRACT? HOW? I DON'T EVEN *KNOW* THE WOMAN!

YOU'RE *THEATRICAL.* YOU'LL THINK OF SOMETHING.

SPLENDID.

LISTEN FOR *TWO THUMPS.*

TWO *WHAT?*

"...YOUR GUIDE TO THE REALM ECTOPLATHMIC!"

I'M *THORRY,* MITH WINKLE! WOULD YOU LIKE ME TO POUR YOU THOME *TEA,* FIRTHT?

"AND A *THCONE,* IF YOU WILL?"

THERTAINLY. NOW EVERYONE *CONTHENTRATE...*

"THPEAK, OH DEARLY DEPARTED OF THE *THPIRIT WORLD!* WHAT *METHAGE* DO YOU *HAVE* FOR UTH TODAY...?"

BEWARE OF THE *SCONES.*

I AM *TOO* PTHYCHIC. YOU'RE ATH BAD ATH *MOMMY*.

YOU'VE *THEEN* WHAT I CAN *DO*, THIMON. I FOUND THE *GHOTHT OF MARPON LANE* FOR YOU!

WE'VE GONE *OVER* THIS, ADELINE. THERE'S NO SUCH *THING* AS GHOSTS.

Heh.

WHAT YOU *EXPERIENCE* WHEN YOU GO INTO A SELF-HYPNOTIC *STATE*--

TRANTH.

--IS AN INCREASED ELECTROMAGNETIC PERCEPTION OF SOME AS-YET-UNNAMED *ENERGY*.

THAT'S WHY I'VE COME TO YOU, *TODAY*, IN FACT. TELL ME...

...HAVE YOU ANY EXPERIENCE WITH *LEY LINES*?

NO.

THUMP THUMP

HEAVENS! WHAT'S THAT *RACKET*? ADDIE?

ADELINE BETHESMA DEWINTER! WHAT HAVE YOU GOTTEN INTO *NOW*?

ANSWER ME!

*A*ND THAT--

--IS MY CUE TO *LEAVE*. WHAT AN *ORDEAL*.

STILL, IT MIGHT BE *WORTH* IT IF I CAN SEE SIMON SHINNY DOWN A *DRAINPIPE*...

ANTAEUS, LOOK WHO IT IS!

SIMON, DON'T MAKE A SCENE...!

YOU NEEDN'T *WARN* ME AS IF I WERE A *SCHOOLCHILD*, EMMA.

I'M NOT WARNING HIM. I'M PROTECTING HIM.

I AND I ALONE KNOW THAT THE BARONESS POSSESSES SORCEROUS ABILITIES THE LIMITS OF WHICH I'VE NOT SEEN TESTED. I'VE WITNESSED THEM WITH MY OWN EYES.

PLEASE TO MAKE NO FURTHER *EXCUSES* FOR *IGNORING* ME, DEAR MAN. YOU *PROMISED* TO COME BY AND PERUSE THE COLLECTION OF *CLIPPINGS* I HAVE ASSEMBLED REGARDING YOUR... *EXPLOITS*, YES?

I FEAR, HOWEVER, THAT THE BARONESS WOULD GLADLY EXPOSE US BOTH IF IT MEANT SPURRING ME TO ACTION.

SUBTEXT? YOU MEAN YOU REALLY AREN'T *AWARE*, SIMON? WOULD YOU CARE FOR AN *EDUCATION*?

SIMON KNOWS *ALL* HE *NEEDS* TO KNOW ABOUT *YOU*, BARONESS.

I HIGHLY *DOUBT* THAT. WHY, THERE ARE ALL *SORTS* OF SECRETS LURKING UNDER SIMON'S VERY *NOSE*. FOR *INSTANCE*—

SIMON, WE'RE WASTING VALUABLE *TIME* HERE. LET'S GO.

I'VE NOT **DISCLOSED** HER CAPABILITIES TO SIMON, NOR DO I **WISH** TO. NOT ONLY WOULD I HAVE TO FACE HIS **SKEPTICISM**--

-- BUT TO **TELL** HIM WOULD BE TO ADMIT I HAVE CERTAIN...**POWERS** ...OF MY **OWN**--

BARONESS, **REMOVE** YOUR HANDS FROM MY PARTNER, OR I SHALL REMOVE THEM **FOR**--

--POWERS THE BARONESS PROMISED TO **THIEVE** FROM ME THE NEXT TIME THEY'RE **USED**. I CANNOT EVEN **TOUCH** HER WITHOUT RISKING A VERY **TELLING DISPLAY OF ENERGY**.

-- YOU.

TROUBLE, EMMA, DARLING? FEEL **FREE** TO...I BELIEVE THE PHRASE IS, "PUT ME IN MY **PLACE**."

ONLY AS **I** SEE FIT, MIRANDA.

BEGGING YOUR **PARDON**, BUT WOULD YOU TWO PLEASE **REPEAT** THAT EXCHANGE? I CAN BARELY **HEAR** IT OVER THE CLAMOR OF **MYSTERIOUS SUBTEXT**.

SHED NO **CROCODILE TEARS** AT MY **DEPARTURE**, BARONESS. I FEEL QUITE **CONFIDENT** THAT OUR PATHS WILL INTERWEAVE **QUITE** SOON.

IN THE MEANTIME, YOU'LL HAVE TO BE CONTENT WITH YOUR **CLIPPINGS**.

Oh, I **SHALL**. IN FACT, ANTAEUS HAS FOUND YET **MORE** NEWS REGARDING THE GREAT SIMON ARCHARD...

...FRESH OFF THE PRESS.

The PENNY ARCADIAN

Copiously Illustrated   Afternoon Edition, Price One Penny

FAMED DETECTIVE MURDERS GRAND DAME

MON ARCHARD SLAYS LADY PENELOPE WAINSCOT

ANDSOME BOUNTY OFFERED

THE LADY WAINSCOTT? BUT THAT'S NOT--

TRUE? IT'S QUITE *FULL* OF *ONE* TRUTH.

THAT SHE WOULD, OF *COURSE,* HAVE *MURCHISON* AS *WELL.* COME *ALONG,* EMMA...

"...THINGS ARE ABOUT TO GET *MUCH* WORSE."

THAT'S HIM!

I *SEE* 'IM!

Ohhh--! THE *MONSTER!*

ALLUS *FIGGERED* HE'D TURN SOMEDAY, I DID.

POLICE! *POLICE!*

GRAB HIM!

HOY, NOW! *I'LL* GET HIM! I GOTS A *FINE REWARD* RUNNIN' RIGHT *TOWARDS* ME!

WAINSCOTT *MANOR?*

SIMON, HAVE YOU TAKEN LEAVE OF YOUR *SENSES?* PERHAPS THE ALLEGED *CRIME SCENE* ISN'T THE BEST PLACE TO *BE AT THE MOMENT...?*

AS OPPOSED TO WHERE *ELSE?* BESIDES, THIS PLACE WILL BE *TEEMING* WITH CLUES THAT WILL *EXPOSE* THIS PATHETIC FRAME, EMMA.

I DOUBT THE *BODY* IS STILL HERE, BUT--

--BUT I COULD BE *WRONG!* LADY WAINSCOTT!

SIMON? *ELLA? THIS* IS AN UNEXPECTED SURPRISE! WHAT BRINGS THE TWO OF *YOU* HERE?

UUULLPP--!

CONGRATULATIONS. USE IT TO BUY A NEW CAB.

CLIMB IN! HURRY!

IF THE COMMISSIONER IS MIRANDA'S PUPPET AS WELL, THEN HIS OFFICERS ARE DOUBTLESS CONVERGING ON US EVEN AS WE--

FWEEEEEEE

HE'S GETTIN' AWAY! AFTER 'IM!

YOU DO. YOU'RE IN DEADLY DANGER, AGATHA--MOST LIKELY FROM YOUR OWN HUSBAND. WHERE IS HE?

I WISH I KNEW, DEAR. I COULD HAVE SWORN HE SAID HE WAS GOING INTO TOWN FOR SOME SNUFF, BUT I MUST HAVE MISHEARD.

I FOUND QUITE AN ABUNDANCE IN THE GIFT BOX THE BARONESS SENT HIM.

THAT'S RIGHT. DON'T BREATHE A WORD, DEAR SIMON, BUT THIS OLD BIDDY ENJOYS A PINCH OR TWO HERSELF FROM TIME TO --

--AIEEEEE!

AGATHA!

CHAPTER 16

Thus Far in Scion

Ethan

Ashleigh

What started with a mysterious sigil led to war. Prince Ethan of the West-ruling Heron Dynasty was graced with a mark granting him power, leading to the accidental scarring of Prince Bron of the East-ruling Raven Dynasty during ritual combat.

Ethan surrendered himself to the Ravens but was soon freed from his imprisonment by a woman named Ashleigh who wanted Ethan to join the Underground cause of freedom for the genetically engineered Lesser Races. Ethan declined her offer and set off for home as war loomed.

When the battle was met, first victory belonged to the Herons, but Ethan's oldest brother and heir to the throne, Artor, was brutally slain by Bron. Ethan vowed to have his revenge and returned to Eastern lands.

The mysterious Mai Shen revealed herself as a member of the godlike First and imbued Bron with a portion of her power. Bron then murdered his father King Viktor, framed Ashleigh – his sister – for the crime and took the throne for himself.

Following a confrontation with Bron, Ethan escaped the Raven Keep accompanied by Ashleigh and his friend Skink. Surviving an encounter with a band of savage Lesser Race outlaws, the group arrived at the Underground's hidden Sanctuary, only to find it destroyed. Amid the destruction, Ethan spied the feared bounty hunter Exeter...

Skink

Bron

Exeter

Kai

Ron **marz** WRITER

Jim **cheung** PENCILER

Don **hillsman II** INKER

Justin **ponsor** COLORIST

Troy **peteri** LETTERER

"SO I SOUGHT OUT THE SANCTUARY, BELIEVING I COULD FIND A MEASURE OF REDEMPTION IN THE UNDERGROUND'S CAUSE.

"NOT A TERRIBLY DIFFICULT TASK. I WOULDN'T BE MUCH OF A BOUNTY HUNTER IF I DIDN'T KNOW WHERE MOST OF THE RUNNERS WERE GOING.

"I'VE HUNTED THE LESSER RACES, BEEN A TALE USED TO FRIGHTEN CHILDREN. OF COURSE MY ARRIVAL INSTILLED FEAR.

"THEN THE RAVEN ARMY BURST INTO THE SANCTUARY, ASHLEIGH'S BROTHER KORT LEADING IT.

THE SANCTUARY WAS FILLED WITH REFUGEES, NOT WARRIORS. WOMEN AND CHILDREN, THE AGED AND THE LAME, ALL PUT TO THE SWORD.

"I DID ALL I COULD. BUT NOT NEARLY ENOUGH.

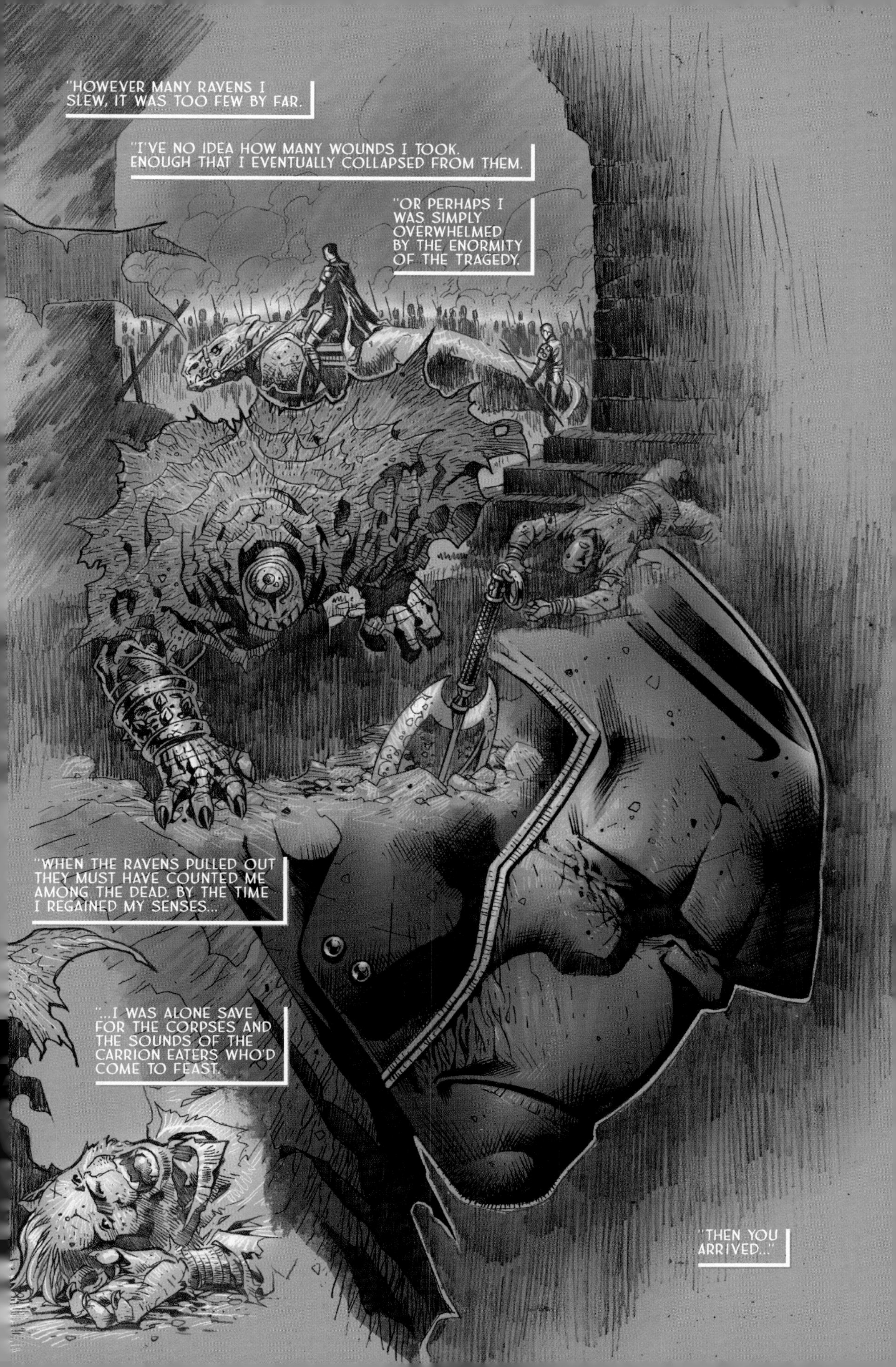
"HOWEVER MANY RAVENS I SLEW, IT WAS TOO FEW BY FAR.
"I'VE NO IDEA HOW MANY WOUNDS I TOOK. ENOUGH THAT I EVENTUALLY COLLAPSED FROM THEM.
"OR PERHAPS I WAS SIMPLY OVERWHELMED BY THE ENORMITY OF THE TRAGEDY.
"WHEN THE RAVENS PULLED OUT THEY MUST HAVE COUNTED ME AMONG THE DEAD. BY THE TIME I REGAINED MY SENSES...
"...I WAS ALONE SAVE FOR THE CORPSES AND THE SOUNDS OF THE CARRION EATERS WHO'D COME TO FEAST.
"THEN YOU ARRIVED..."

ASHLEIGH?

DO YOU UNDERSTAND WHAT REALLY HAPPENED HERE?

KORT CARRIED OUT THIS CARNAGE, BUT I'M SURE BRON ORDERED IT. AND AT LEAST PART OF IT WAS BECAUSE OF *ME*.

BRON DID THIS TO CRIPPLE THE UNDERGROUND, AND BECAUSE *I'M* PART OF IT.

I WANTED TO SAVE THESE PEOPLE...

...AND LOOK WHAT I BROUGHT UPON THEM.

WE *WILL* REBUILD WHAT WE HAD. THERE ARE OTHERS WHO BELIEVE.

THIS *ISN'T* THE END OF THE UNDERGROUND.

I WAS SUPPOSED TO LEAD A MISSION INTO THE KORINAR MOUNTAINS.

A DOZEN OF US PLANNED TO DESTROY A GENETICS FACILITY MY DYNASTY WAS SECRETLY KEEPING OPERATIONAL.

"My hovership swept the ocean's roiling surface, pointed east. At the horizon, only the vastness of the Great Sea's unbroken swells. And beyond that, beyond the crimson sunrises, my true destination: war and black, bloody death."

From the logbooks of Admiral Edvin of the Heron Dynasty

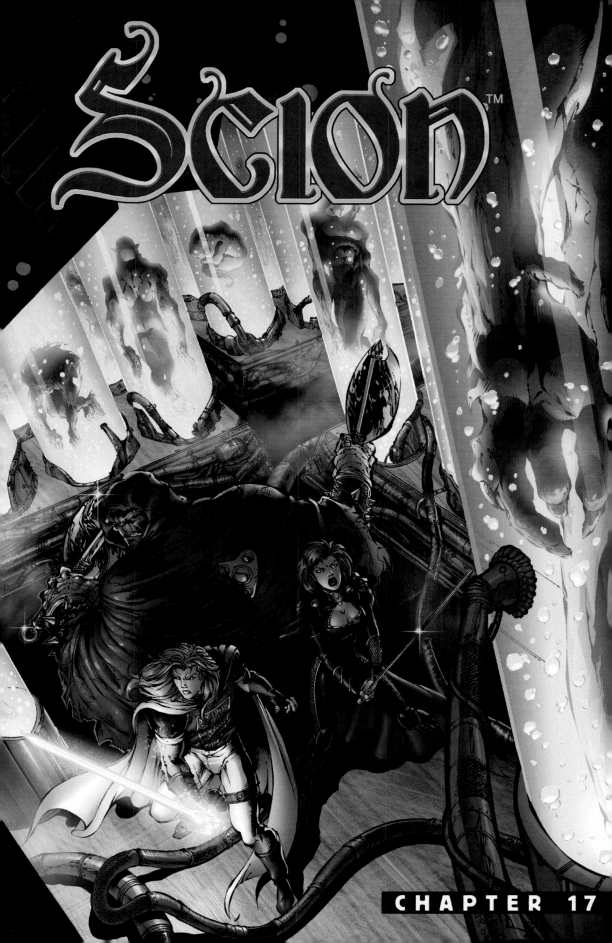

Chapter 17
by

Ron
marz
WRITER

Andrea
Di Vito
PENCILER

Rob
Hunter
INKER

Jason
Lambert
COLORIST

Troy
peteri
LETTERER

IT'S ALL RIGHT...

...WE'RE ALONE.

I STILL DON'T UNDERSTAND. THERE AREN'T ANY GUARDS? ANYWHERE?

WHY WOULD THERE BE?

WHO IN THEIR RIGHT MIND WOULD WANT TO BREAK *IN* TO THIS PLACE?

I NEVER...

...*NEVER* IMAGINED ANYTHING LIKE THIS.

NOT IN ANY NIGHTMARE.

THOSE OUTLAWS WHO ATTACKED US ON OUR JOURNEY NORTH, *THEY* WERE SPAWNED HERE.

ALL THIS IS THE PRODUCT OF ONE MAN. DOCTOR TYRRUS.

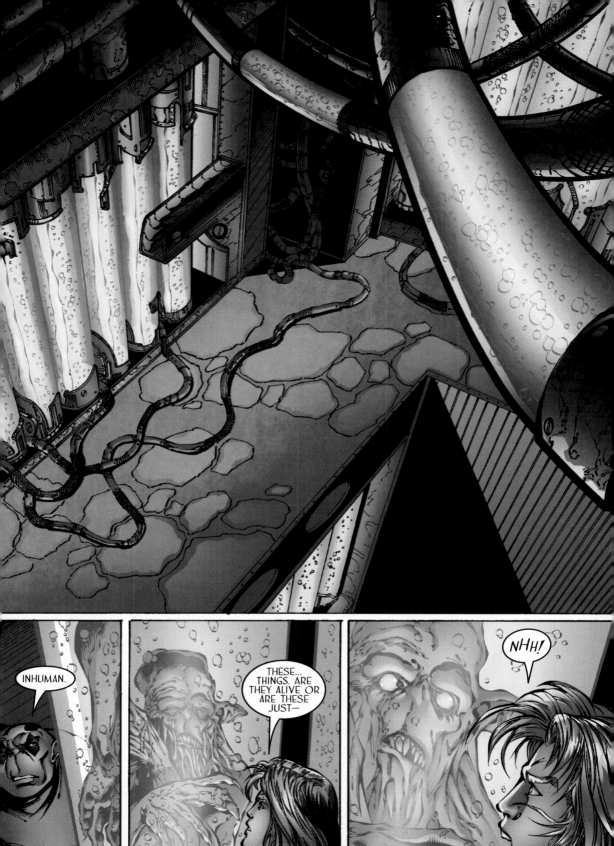

INHUMAN.

THESE... THINGS. ARE THEY ALIVE OR ARE THESE JUST—

NHH!

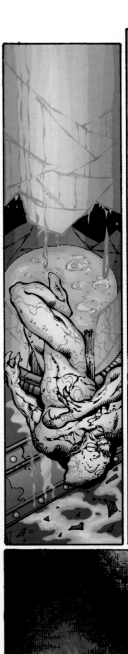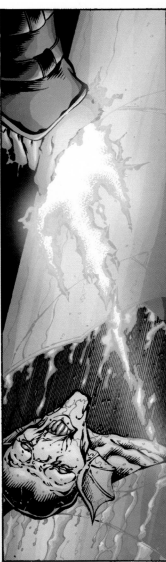

ETHAN.

IT WAS THE RIGHT THING TO DO.

I UNDERSTAND THAT.

BUT IT DOESN'T MAKE HAVING DONE IT ANY EASIER TO ACCEPT.

OUR STORY SO FAR...

SAM

ROIYA

JeMERIK

ZANNIATI

TCHLUSARUD

KHYRADON

FOR CENTURIES, the five human worlds of the Planetary Union have been at war with the lizardlike Saurians of Tcharun, unable to find a weapon formidable enough to turn the tide of battle.

And then along came Sam.

A mustered-out soldier with a good heart, SAMANDAHL REY and his fellow ex-soldier ROIYA SINTOR came looking for work on the neutral world Tanipal only to be ambushed by Sam's Saurian enemy TCHLUSARUD. In the ensuing battle, they picked up two crucial allies — the mysterious JeMERIK MEER (smitten by Roiya) and ZANNI (a spy anxious to escape the harem of Tanipal's Sultan). Victory, though, came not from any of them but rather from a strange sigil, a brand of vast power burned into Sam's chest by a vanishing stranger. In fact, Sam first realized the sigil's potential the moment Roiya was slain — and Sam, in a moment of anguished grief, neutralized the attack by unintentionally unleashing a half-mile wide explosion of matter-transforming force.

Once Sam, JeMerik and Zanni escaped Tanipal, however, an over-wrought Sam learned that all was not lost; while Roiya's lifeless body lay in stasis aboard Sam's starship, the *BitterLuck*, her mind and soul had been "uploaded" into the ship's computers seconds before her death, allowing Roiya to live on in holographic form. Now the two of them are taking point in defending the human race from the merciless Saurian army.

PREVIOUSLY...
In his new position as Field Commander of the Union Army, Sam prepares to lead the fleet against a Saurian blitzkrieg, unaware that the Saurians aren't the only ones gunning for him....

Mark **WAID** *WRITER*
Scot **EATON** *PENCILER*
Andrew **HENNESSY** *INKER*
Wil **QUINTANA** *COLORIST*
Dave **LANPHEAR** *LETTERER*

"WHERE IS SAMANDAHL REY?"

NNNNNNHH...

... GRASS?

WHY AM I LOOKING AT--?

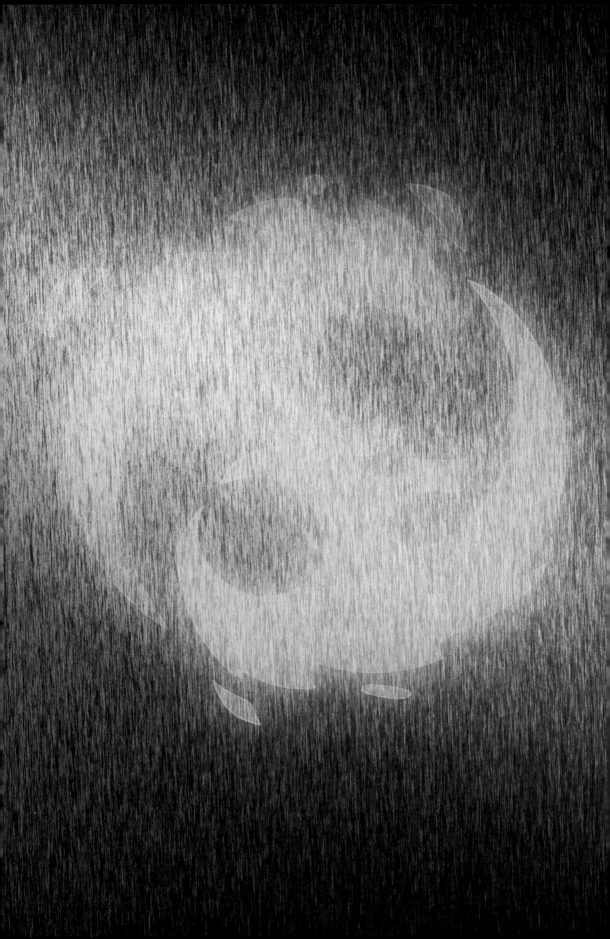

HE LOOKS AS CONFUSED AS I AM...AND BEIN' SMACK IN THE MIDDLE OF BATTLE ISN'T CLEARIN' *ANYONE'S* HEAD.

SO *THAT'S* GOTTA STOP.

AND SINCE I DON'T SPEAK THE LANGUAGE, THE ONLY WAY I KNOW OF TO BREAK UP SOMETHIN' LIKE *THIS*--

ᏔᎻᎪᎢᏕ ᎻᎬ ᎠᎾᏆᏁᎶᏕ

ᏴᎪᎾᏦ ᎢᎻᎬᏢᎬ···

--IS T'GIVE *BOTH* SIDES SOMETHIN' TO BE AFRAID OF!

THE ONES WHO RUN ARE OBVIOUSLY THE VISITING TEAM. THE **LOCALS** ARE THE ONES ACTIN' LIKE I'M A **GOD**-- I GUESS--I CAN'T UNDERSTAND A WORD THEY'RE **SAYIN'**--WHICH IS FLATTERIN', BUT I DON'T **CARE**--

--BECAUSE IT AIN'T GETTIN' ME **HOME!** WHAT **HAPPENED?** HOW DID KHYRADON 'PORT ME **AWAY?**

WHAT'S GOING **ON** HERE?

"SO HARD DID IT *SEIZE* ME, IT CRUSHED THE *AIR* FROM MY *LUNGS*...AND YET, I HEARD *SCREAMING*."

"...IN A VOICE NOT MY *OWN*."

"THE IDOL'S GRIP FILLED MY EARS WITH THE CRY OF A *MILLION VOICES*...SEARED MY *HEART* WITH THE FIRE OF A BILLION *EMOTIONS*.

"THE HUNGER OF AN *INFANT*. THE *LONELINESS* OF A *DYING MAN*.

"THE MEANING OF THE BULL'S RASP AND THE BLACKSMITH'S *SCOWL*. IN THAT INSTANT, I UNDERSTOOD IT *ALL*...

"...ONLY TO *AWAKE*...THOSE SENSATIONS FADING LIKE THE MEMORIES OF A *DREAM*.

"*FADING*...BUT NOT *EVAPORATING*.

"FROM THAT NIGHT *ON*, THE *BRAND* LEFT UPON MY CHEST RENDERED UNTO ME A CERTAIN...*EMPATHY*.

"A UNIQUE GIFT FOR *COMMUNICATION*, BE IT AN ABILITY TO READ *DESIRES* AND MEDIATE *PEACE*...

"...OR ANTICIPATE THE STRATEGY OF THE *ENEMY*...THE MOVES OF ANY COMBATANT WHO DARED *FACE* ME IN *COMBAT*."

GAIA.
UNION HOMEWORLD.

-- TELL THE *COMMUNICATIONS MINISTER* I SAID *NOW.* AND SAY IT *LOUDER* TO THE DELASSIAN *TREASURY.*

"...*REPLY IMMEDIATELY.*" ADD MY SIGNATURE.

HMM.

SIR?

Oh. NOTHING, BONNI.

JUST OBSERVING *ZANNIATI.* FOR A DARK HORSE *POLITICO,* SHE'S PROVING HERSELF *ADMIRABLY...*

MR. PRESIDENT, SIR, OUR SOLDIERS HAVE *RETURNED.*

THE CREW OF THE *BITTERLUCK* HAS REQUESTED AN IMMEDIATE *AUDIENCE.*

MR. PRESIDENT... ZANNI...WE REGRET TO REPORT LOSSES IN EXCESS OF SIXTY PERCENT. AND THAT'S NOT *ALL.*

AND *SAM?*

ZANNI...

"...WE HAVE SOMETHING TO *TELL* YOU..."

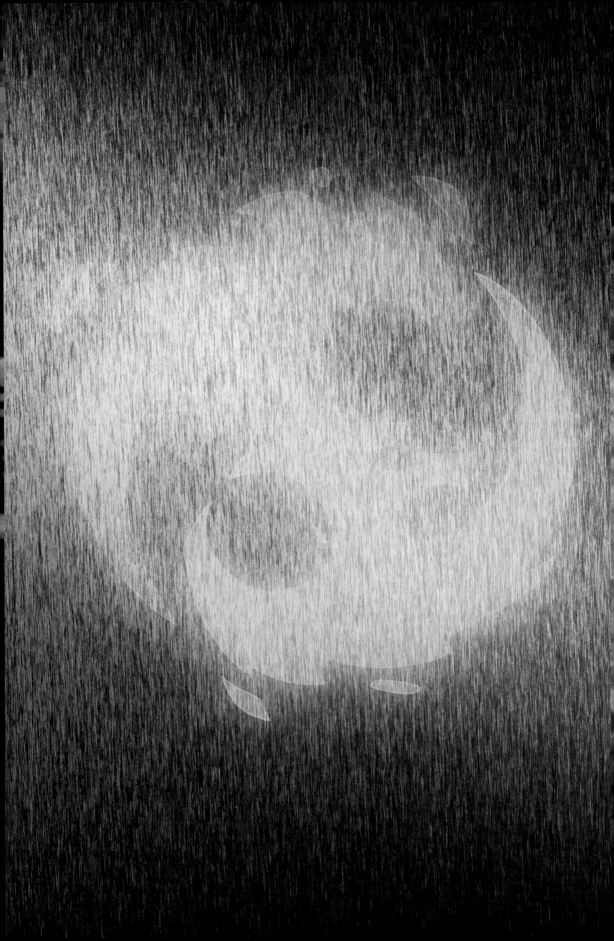

...NOW.

THANKS. THREAT *NEUTRALIZED*, MR. PRESIDENT.

THOOM

SAY IT *AGAIN*, SAM. YOU'RE OPEN *ACROSS ALL UNION FREQUENCIES.*

OUR MEN ARE LISTENING BECAUSE THEY'RE GETTING HIT *HARD* AND THEY NEED TO HEAR FROM *YOU.* WHERE *ARE* WE? WHAT'S THE GOOD *WORD*?

FROM THE *TOP*, SIR...

"...*TCHLUSARUD* IS RACING *KHYRADON* TO FIND LOSER'S MOTHER. KHYRADON THOUGHT HE GRABBED THE *THRONE* BY KILLING THE OLD BROAD, BUT WE HAVE... *INFORMATION* THAT SHE'S *ALIVE.*

"WE MAY BE ABLE TO MAKE SOMETHING OUT OF THAT IF WE CAN *PLAY* IT RIGHT.

"*ZANNIATI'S* SET UP AN UNDERGROUND SUPPLY NETWORK ON *DELASSIA.* THEIR IMPORTS HAVE BEEN CUT OFF BY THE SAURIANS TO KEEP DELASSIA FROM CRANKING OUT MORE SUPER*ARC* DRIVES -- BUT THAT WON'T STOP *ZANNI.*

"*JEMERIK MEER* IS WITH *ME*, AND WE'RE ON OUR WAY TO *BREJHUR* NEXT, TO BACK OUR SOLDIERS *THERE.* IF YOU'RE *LISTENING*, BOYS -- BE READY TO *RALLY.* OVER AND *OUT.*"

SHHKKK

ЯЯЯЯЯ!

THYMП

-- YOU'D BE *DEAD*.

THEIR LEADER **BRATH** GETS IT. I HAVE NO CLUE WHY HE AND I CAN COMMUNICATE, OTHER'N THE FACT HE SPORTS A BRAND LIKE **MINE**...FOR REASONS **NEITHER** OF US CAN DOPE OUT.

AROUND HERE, QUESTIONS OUTNUMBER **ANSWERS** A HUNDRED TO **ONE**. ALL I KNOW FOR **SURE** IS THAT BRATH'S ARMY IS IN **TROUBLE**.

I AM **IMPRESSED**, SAM. IN JUST UNDER THREE **NIGHTFALLS**, YOU HAVE TAUGHT MY MEN **MUCH** ABOUT YOUR WAYS OF COMBAT.

I KNOW A FEW TRICKS. READY TO **RIDE**?

YES. I WISH TO SEE THE SCOPE OF THE *ENEMY* WITH MY *OWN* EYES.

IT IS GOOD TO HAVE AN *ALLY*, SAM. DO YOU SUPPOSE THERE ARE *OTHERS* OUT THERE... *LIKE* US?

DUNNO. THE UNIVERSE IS PRETTY DAMN *BIG*, BRATH. TAKE IT FROM SOMEBODY WHO'S POKED *AROUND* UP THERE.

UP...?

IN THE *STARS*? YOU'VE TRAVELED THE *STARS*? HOW? *WHEN*?

OKAY... I TOLD YOU I'VE BEEN A *SOLDIER*, RIGHT...?

FOR THE NEXT HOUR OR SO, I *YAMMER* ABOUT MY ARMY CAREER. TO HIS *CRED*, BRATH LISTENS *PATIENTLY* EVEN WHEN HE DOESN'T QUITE *GET* IT.

EVEN WHEN *I* DON'T QUITE GET IT.

...OVERSTAYED MY *WELCOME* BY ABOUT *TWO YEARS*, GIVE OR TAKE. DON'T GET ME *WRONG*. IT'S NOT A *BAD* PLACE T'*WORK*...

...IT'S JUST THAT, AS TIME WENT BY, THE *SAURIANS* GOT T'BE MORE AND MORE *FRUSTRATING* TO THE *HIGH COMMAND*...A PROBLEM THEY COULDN'T *SOLVE*...

...SO THEY'D TURN ON *US*, LOOKIN' FOR "*PROBLEMS*" THEY *COULD* SOLVE. HUMAN *NATURE*. GAVE 'EM THE ILLUSION OF *CONTROL* T'GO LOOKIN' FOR *CRISES*. DON'T KNOW *WHY* I COULDN'T JUST LET IT ROLL *OFF*...

...BUT WHEN *BUDGET CUTS* COST MY MEN SOME *DUE PROMOTIONS*, I HIT THE *ROOF*. ROIYA SAYS WE WERE *MUSTERED OUT*. I SAY I *QUIT*. WE'RE *STILL* ARGUING *THAT* POINT.

ANYWAY, A COUPLE YEARS GO *BY*, AND *BOOM*...I GET THIS *SIGIL* PLANTED ON ME. SPEAKING OF *WHICH*... *SAVAL*, YOU SAID YOU MIGHT HAVE SOME *INFO*...?

BALDY THE *PHILOSOPHER* HAS HIS OWN "*MAGICKS*," AS HE PUTS IT, TO BRIDGE THE *LANGUAGE GAP*, AND I LISTEN HARD. I *WANNA* LEARN ABOUT THIS...

THIS *INSIGNIA*...CLEARLY, IT IS BESTOWED UPON THOSE WITH GREAT *POTENTIAL*.

O-KAY... ...

WAIT. THAT'S *IT*? THAT'S YOUR *INFORMATION*?

NO. IT IS MY *OBSERVATION*. *HERE* IS MY INFORMATION. ARE YOU *PREPARED*?

ABSOLUTELY.

THEN LISTEN *CLOSELY* AND *CAREFULLY*, SAMANDAHL REY. I WILL SPEAK *ONE WORD*. ONE *CRUCIAL WORD* THAT IS THE *SUMMATION* OF ALL THAT *WAS*, *IS*, AND *WILL BE*.

"*BALANCE*."

EΦEPXONE ΓATHEP TOΓETHEP NOW+

MOYNT XOYP HOPCEC ANΔ PIΔE+ WE HEAΔ TO THE MOYNTAINC+

TRANSLATION: WE'RE *SCREWED.*

AGREED, TANIELLA. AS UNTHINKABLE AS IT *SOUNDS,* WE MUST *RETREAT.* I CANNOT LET MY OWN *PRIDE* COST THESE MEN THEIR *LIVES.*

GANTH, HORNOTH... GATHER OUR *STEEDS* AND OUR *SUPPLIES* AND DO IT *NOW.*

GANTH?

TOO LATE.

DELASSIA.

MADAME AMBASSADOR, THE UNDERGROUND JUST DECRYPTED THIS SAURIAN *EMBARGO ORDER*. YOU NEED TO READ IT...

...AND I WISH I KNEW A WORD MORE URGENT THAN "IMMEDIATELY."

A RATION ON *COMMON NETERIUM?* BUT THAT'S CRUCIAL TO THE *SUPERARC'S FUNCTIONALITY!* IT'S AS IF THEY *KNEW* THAT-- BUT *HOW?*

IT'S A *BLOW*, AGREED. THE SAURIANS ARE ENACTING SOME PRETTY BAFFLING *STRATEGIES*.

REPORTEDLY, THEIR NEW *MINISTER OF TRADE* IS ABOUT TO TELECAST AN ADDRESS TO THE OVERGROUND DELASSIANS--THOSE LEFT ALIVE, AT LEAST.

I'LL RIG THE *VIEWSCREEN* TO RECEIVE THE BROADCAST. MAYBE WE CAN *LEARN* SOMETHING.

I DON'T--

IT'S AS IF THE SAURIANS ARE GOING OUT OF THEIR *WAY* TO DENY US CRITICAL *SUPERARC* SUPPLIES--BUT THAT MAKES *NO SENSE*.

THE ONLY WAY THEY COULD SINGLE OUT SUCH OTHERWISE-INNOCUOUS *COMPONENTS* WOULD BE TO *OBTAIN* A DRIVE--BUT *HOW?* WHO AMONG THEM COULD BE *CLEVER* ENOUGH TO--

--PROUD TO AT LAST ANNOUNCE MY *FULL* AND UNCONDITIONAL *ALLIANCE* WITH TOMORROW'S *GALACTIC LEADERS*.

AS MINISTER OF *TRADE*, I CAN BRING THE DELASSIANS TO THEIR *KNEES*--AND I *WILL*--

IN THE BEGINNING...

They were the First.
From their home, Elysia, they held power
over all. Worlds were created at their touch, and their
only threat was each other. Now the twin towers of the old city
and the new city, separated by the Eidolon rift, are united in a new anxiety:
the ennui of centuries has catalyzed into fear with the discovery of
the Sigil-Bearers, beings with powers the First did not bestow.

Three members of the High Council of each House met secretly within the Eidolon itself
to share information about the phenomenon of these newly-powered mortals.

INGRA
the SEETHING BEAUTY

Trenin the Hunter sought out the Sigil-Bearer Samandahl Rey,
who was inexplicably able to steal power from the hunter's
own personal store:

Trenin led a hunting party to the world of the Warlord
Todosi, where the Sigil-Bearer was leading the army of
Nayado in an unwinnable war against the more numerous
armies of Shinacea. The encounter led to the death of
Todosi and the death of the Secundae Kerspan,
and the loss of Altwaal's weapon,
left behind on that world.

PYREM
the DIPLOMAT

ORIUM
the ORACLE

GANNISH
the SUFFERER

YALA
the WARRIOR WOMAN

TRENIN
the HUNTER

PERSHA
She looks to her
father for aid...

SEAHN
He relies on no one
but himself...

Prodded by Enson and watched
by Persha, Seahn murders Laia,
a fellow Secundae who won't
bow to his will. Wyture suggests
to Persha that she has a secret
way to cross the Eidolon rift.
Ingra meets the visiting Ilahn of
Demetria, gaining another
potential ally. Gannish pursues
a star in search of answers, and
Yala informs Pyrem and Trenin
of Persha's search for Altwaal.

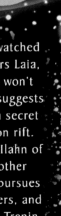

Barbara
KESEL
WRITER

Bart
SEARS
PENCILER

Andy
SMITH
INKER

Michael
ATIYEH
COLORIST

Dave
LANPHEAR
LETTERER

I DON'T *ENJOY* HAVING TO BE SO HARSH...

...BUT I'M DOING WHAT MUST BE DONE. YOU CAN SEE THAT, CAN'T YOU?

YOU MAKE IT SOUND SO *SIMPLE.*

IT *IS* SIMPLE. *CHOOSE,* KWE.

...OR NEW WAYS, AND *LIFE.* DO YOU WANT TO BE SECOND FOREVER...

...OR TO BE *FIRST.*

LOOK WITHIN-- WHAT DOES YOUR HEART TELL YOU?

CHOOSE THE OLD WAYS AND OUR DEATH AT THE HANDS OF THESE SIGIL-BEARERS...

CHOOSE.

THEN, AFTER *INGRA* POUNDS DOWN HOUSE DEXTER--

--A REUNITED ELYSIA WILL BE HUNGRY FOR A *STRONG* AND *FAIR* LEADER--

WHO'S *THIS*?

INGRA! I DIDN'T EXPECT TO HAVE *YOU* COME TO *ME*.

BRAAG! AM I UNWELCOME?

OF COURSE NOT!

GIVE US SOME ROOM, WILL YOU, CELYN?

GOOD, BECAUSE I'D HATE TO *IMPOS* ON YOUR LITTL INSURRECTION.

A MAN'S GOT TO HAVE A BACK-UP PLAN, INGRA.

I EXPECT NO LESS OF YOU, BRAAG. I WOULDN'T HAVE *CHOSEN* YOU IF YOU COULDN'T OFFER ME A CHALLENGE.

BRAAG, I'D LIKE YOU TO MEET MY OTHER CHALLENGE, *SEAHN* OF *DEXTER*...

...ISN'T HE *FAMILIAR?*

YOU *DO* REMIND ME OF SOMEBODY.

A CREATURE OF BOTH HOUSES

BECAUSE OF A VISION I WITNESSED.

WHICH WAS...?

I SAW THE TWO HOUSES COME TOGETHER INTO ONE SIGIL WHEN I WATCHED YOUR HUNTING PARTY SLAY THE SIGIL-BEARER TODOSI--

-- AAAH --

STOP.

YOU'VE ALREADY SAID ENOUGH-- YOU CAN'T LIE TO AN EMPATH.

SO YOU CAN LOOK RIGHT THROUGH OUR EYES AND WE DON'T EVEN KNOW YOU'RE THERE.

YOU'VE BEEN SPYING ON US--

-- HOW MUCH HAVE YOU SEEN?

AH... UH...

AT LEAST YOU HAVE THE GRACE TO BE CHAGRINED.

YOU'VE TURNED OUT REMARKABLY WELL, CONSIDERING WHO RAISED YOU.

YOU WILL *NOT* DISPARAGE MY MOTHER!

WELL...*THAT'S* A FAMILIAR TEMPER.

ALTWAAL SAID THOSE SAME WORDS!

YOU CREATED A CREATURE OF BOTH HOUSES!

MATED TO YOUR OWN EMPATHY. DON'T YOU RECOGNIZE YOUR OWN NATURE, PYREM?

WITH A PAIR OF ABLE LIEUTENANTS LIKE YOU TWO, WHAT MORE DO I NEED TO CONQUER ELYSIA?

DON'T WORRY, BRAAG. YOU'RE MY FAVORITE.

HAVE YOUR FORCES PREPARED FOR ACTION.

WHEN IT'S TIME TO STRIKE, I WANT YOU READY.

WE'LL *BE* READY.

LET'S JUST GET IT RIGHT THIS TIME. THE YEARS AFTER THE RIFT ARE AN ERA I DON'T WANT TO RELIVE.

HE'S NOT GOING TO MARCH OVER AND INTERFERE WITH *MY* HOUSE, IS HE?

NO.

BRAAG'S ALWAYS MORE *ATTENTIVE* IF HE THINKS THERE'S GOING TO BE A FIGHT.

I JUST WANT TO KEEP HIM OCCUPIED AND INTERESTED.

DON'T WORRY, SEAHN. YOU'RE MY FAVORITE.

SEAHN... HE'S...

...THERE'S A *TAINT* TO HIM NOW.

ENSON?

WHAT HAS SEAHN *DONE?*

FOLLOWED THE EXAMPLE SET BY ANOTHER.

FOLLOW THE IMAGE I SEND...

...TO SEE FOR YOURSELF.

OH!

THIS WOMAN IS... DEAD.

HOW STRANGE, WHAT I'M FEELING.

I FIND MYSELF REGRETTING THE LOSS OF LIFE...

...THE WASTE OF POTENTIAL...

...AS THOUGH THE INDIVIDUAL HAD AS MUCH VALUE AS THE WHOLE.

IT WAS THE NECESSARY SACRIFICE.

OUR GOAL CANNOT BE ACHIEVED WITHOUT LOSS.

There exists in each of us the capacity to rearrange our forms to suit our desires.

There are those marks that must be borne —

The evidence of another's will asserting dominance over our own —

Mine are solely the result of my stubborn refusal to erase the violent patterning of my flesh...

My face and limbs are tattered with the cruel reminders of my struggle against the rift's creation.

I bear my scars voluntarily.

...the ever-present reminder of my hubris.

Once I dared to suggest that we First were the governors of our own creation and should evolve to a state of communal authority, abolishing the tradition of fealty to one leader and assuming an equality with Altwaal.

My revolution led not to a golden age but to a city divided and the era of a fiercer god among gods.

Additional justification for my fleshly reminders.

CHAPTER 12
BY

Barbara
KESEL
WRITER

Andrea
DI VITO
PENCILER

Rob
HUNTER
INKER

Jason
LAMBERT
COLORIST

Dave
LANPHEAR
LETTERER

Cover Colors by Michael Atiyeh

The melancholy of their loneliness calls to me—

Details are the province of investigation or interrogation, but I can sense they have survived a great loss.

They differ from us in one substantial mode of manner...

...they do not love conflict. They flinch from it, both in action and interaction.

My beloved Yala would find their techniques inelegant, their tactics crude...

...but they sufficed to bring the battle I witnessed to a conclusion favoring this small battalion.

REMEMBER YOUR VOWS...

...YOU'VE ALL PROMISED TO STEP UP AND SUPPORT ME WHEN I GIVE THE SIGNAL.

IF YOU BEGIN TO QUAVER IN YOUR RESOLVE, JUST THINK BACK TO WHERE WE ARE NOW...

WE WOULDN'T WANT ANY MORE DEAD BODIES TURNING UP IN THE PLAZA.

WELL DONE, SEAHN.

NOT YET--TELL ME THAT WHEN YOU CALL ME LEADER, ENSON...

...SOON.

Next month in
EDGE

THE FIRST
Chapters 13 & 14
Pyrem and Seahn set down the road to confrontation.

MYSTIC
Chapters 18 & 19
It's the return of Animora, lovelier and deadlier than ever!

RUSE
Chapter 4
Miranda's schemes culminate with a literal bang!

SCION
Chapters 18 - 20
Ethan is reunited with his brother and sister — but for how long?

SIGIL
Chapters 19 & 20
Sam's team up with Brath sends him bouncing to still more worlds.

SAURIANS - UNNATURAL SELECTION
Chapter 1
*From the world of **SIGIL**, a mini-series that reminds us you are what you eat!*

If you've just been following EDGE, you're only getting one half of the Compendia experience. Over the following pages, we'll introduce you to the ongoing series that make up FORGE, the *other* "Monthly Comics For Your Bookshelf."™

Like EDGE, every volume of FORGE features at least five continuing stories in an inexpensive but attractive trade paperback format. And, like every other CrossGen book, FORGE is a superhero-free zone of action, intrigue, and adventure.

A Sword And Sorcery Epic

Hundreds of years ago, the Five Lands joined together to end the tyranny of Mordath. Now a mysterious force has brought him back from the dead, this time with magic powers. With a troll army at his back, Mordath soon puts the Five Lands under his heel. He is the unchallenged master of the world. Only one woman has eluded his iron grip. And with that one woman rests the sole hope of ending Mordath's reign of terror.

SOJOURN is the story of Arwyn, a woman whose quest for vengeance began in the fires that engulfed her city. Arwyn's one aim is to slay Mordath, but to do that she must first find the weapon that can kill a man who is already dead. One of CrossGen's most popular titles, SOJOURN takes a fresh approach to classic fantasy themes using some of the best artwork in comics today.

Writer: **Ron Marz**
Penciler: **Greg Land**
Inker: **Drew Geraci**
Colorist: **Caesar Rodriguez**

Beyond the dimensional rift exists an evil known as the Negation, an empire bent on expanding into our reality. They have kidnapped an array of beings from across the CrossGen Universe, condemning them to a prison planet where their strengths and weaknesses can be probed. Lost and without a clue, a small group nevertheless breaks free of their gulag.

They manage to escape under the dubious leadership of Obregon Kaine, a human being without any special powers or abilities who somehow forges them into a team. Kaine convinces them that the only way home is to find, corner, and defeat Charon, the godlike leader of the Negation Empire. It's *The Great Escape* meets *The Dirty Dozen* in a galaxy far, far away

Writer: **Tony Bedard**
Penciler: **Paul Pelletier**
Inker: **Dave Meikis**
Colorist: **James Rochelle**

MERIDIAN is the story of Sephie, a sheltered young girl whose life resembles nothing so much as a fairy tale. The beloved only child of the Minister of Meridian, she grows up with an entire floating city as her playground. Then her father dies, and she inherits a sigil imbued with the power to create. So does her wicked Uncle Ilahn, except that his powers are bent on destruction and domination. Suddenly Sephie finds herself at the center of a power struggle, and quickly she learns that there is more than love in the world.

Kidnapped to the world of Cadador, Sephie's journey home to Meridian puts her in the path of many people, good and bad, that help her grow up and counter Ilahn's plans to take over her world.

Writer: **Barbara Kesel**
Penciler: **Steve McNiven**
Inker: **Tom Simmons**
Colorist: **Morry Hollowell**

On a world wracked by war, only one small island nation stands unconquered. The Warlord Todosi leads his troops to victory in a great and perhaps final battle, only to be betrayed by the gods. His brother, the monk Obo-san, vows vengence, and soon finds himself branded as not only a heretic, but a traitor as well. Obo-san must choose between honor and tradition.

THE PATH is a new take on the samurai tale, a staple of Japanese entertainment with a growing audience here in the West. In addition to all the action and dynamic artwork that typifies the genre, we have the struggle of one man walking the thin line between honor and duty.

Writer: **Ron Marz**
Penciler: **Bart Sears**
Inker: **Mark Pennington**
Colorist: **Michael Atiyeh**